Folens

1

Mary Green

Contents

Introduction

The series *English for the More Able*, books 1–6, has been written for primary school children whose performance is above their chronological age and who need particularly challenging tasks. It is assumed they will have wide reading experience, a good command of language, have acquired problem-solving skills and can work independently. Intervention by the teacher can therefore be minimal.

Book 1 in the series is targeted at children aged 5–6 years. The tasks included in each activity sheet relate to the objectives in the *National Literacy Strategy*, drawing on word, sentence and text levels, and are divided into three terms. However, the activity sheets do not have to be followed in chronological order. You may wish to use them at alternative times throughout the year, according to your needs.

The material and language tasks selected cover a wide range of subjects, genres and writing styles. For example, 'Bramble Lane' in Term 1 focuses on following simple instructions and finding key information, while 'Badger's catch' in Term 3 looks at recognising and learning simple spelling patterns.

The teacher page
Each activity sheet is accompanied by a page of supporting notes giving advice and information about how to use the activities. It is organised under the following sub-headings:

● **Learning objectives**
The skills on which each activity sheet is based are outlined here. Those taken directly from that term of the National Literacy Strategy are in italics. Those that are relevant but from a different term are in Roman type.

● **Activity sheet/Expectations**
This describes the content of the activity sheet, and elaborates on the objectives above. It also gives the teacher an indication of the kinds of skills required by the children and what to expect from them. Examples are often given and, where appropriate, specific answers.

● **Further activities**
Suggestions are offered on how to develop further the skills and tasks detailed in the activity sheets. These may involve extended work (such as creating a booklet over time), research work (such as using ICT) or shorter tasks.

● **Resources**
This lists the relevant activity sheet, together with information on useful equipment and books, such as poems, reference and other non-fiction texts.

Objectives grid
This appears on page 64, and it provides a quick, easy-to-consult guide to the skills covered in the activity sheets.

Exploring rhyme

Learning objectives

Word level
- *To practise and secure the ability to rhyme, and relate this to spelling patterns through:*
  – exploring and playing with rhyming patterns.

Text level
- *To recite stories and rhymes with predictable and repeating patterns, extemporising on patterns orally by substituting words and phrases, extending patterns, inventing patterns and playing with rhyme.*
- *To write down their lines or invented patterns.*

Activity sheet/Expectations

When the children work on the activity sheet, encourage them initially to say or chant the first verse about the rain several times before they begin the additional verses. This will give them the opportunity to become familiar with the rhythm as well as the rhyme. It is assumed the children will have developed some skills in reading and writing so, for example, they have a sound knowledge of short vowel sounds, common vowel digraphs such as 'ee' and 'oo' and consonant blends such as 'br' and 'pl'.

After reading the rhyme, the children are asked to complete the last lines of two more verses by creating their own lines, which should largely depend on rhyme for their effect. For the second, easier, verse, for example, the children may simply repeat the line *But not upon me!* or create their own line, such as *But not on Lee!*, depending on their facility with rhyme. In any case, you can use this variation as a teaching point later.

In the third verse, several appropriate lines might emerge from the suggested words given, providing the children can select the rhyming words *grey*, *play*, *Jay* (for example, *When I go out to play*, *When the skies are grey*, *With my dog, Jay*). If the children can select their own rhyming words, which might include names or be nonsense rhymes, all well and good.

Further activities

The children can make up several more lines to fit the verses and discuss the merits of each from the point of view of sound and meaning.

You may also wish to point to the rhythm of the line, tapping out the beat. For example, contrast the line *When I go out to play* with *When I play* so the children are alerted to the difference.

Use the themes of rain and water to reinforce other sound patterns and help the children create verses or lines, for example *pitter-patter*, *drip/slip* and *wish/wash*. Linking common rhyming words with verse is fun, and the regular rhythm of most simple poems helps the children to recall sounds more easily. Explore other children's rhymes (see 'Resources'), especially those that are focused on daily life, as they can be used to adapt or add verses.

Resources

AS 'The rain'; *The Book of 1000 Poems – The Classic Collection for Children* compiled by J Murray Macbain (Collins)

The rain

Name: .... Date: ....

1. Read this rhyme.

Rain on the green grass,
And rain on the tree;
And rain on the house-top,
But not upon me!

Anon

fly   sea   play
key   knee   Jay   grey

2. Now read this new verse. Finish the last line. Choose from the words in the box above or think of your own.

Rain on the ducks,
Rain on the bee;
Rain on the chimney pot,
But _____

3. Write the last line for this verse. Choose from the words in the box at the top of the page or think of your own.

Rain in the garden,
Rain every day;
Splash in the puddles,

_____

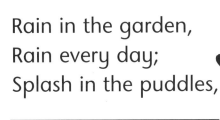

Additional vocabulary

Learning objectives

Word level
- *To read on sight other familiar words* (other than high frequency words identified for Y1 and Y2).

Sentence level
- *To write captions and simple sentences, and to reread, recognising whether or not they make sense, e.g. missing words, wrong word order.*

Activity sheet/Expectations

In this activity, the children are presented with a detailed illustration of a street scene. The name of the town, 'Sunny Vale', is repeated several times and the character of a young boy, Sam, is also included.

The children are asked to read the labels and notices in the picture and to make deductions from their observations. They are also asked to label particular features, without being given the words. If you wish, and according to their ability, the children can then write sentences in reply to the questions, on spare paper. However, it is best if they discuss the details of the illustration first, possibly with a partner.

Further activities

The children can discuss a range of other features related to 'Sunny Vale' and their own experiences. For example:
- Do they attend a swimming pool? If so, is it nearby or must they travel to it?
- Is there a library in their town? When is it open?
- What facilities does their town or local area have that are lacking in the picture?

The illustration can also prompt discussion about Sam, his home, his dog, his potential family and interests.

It is assumed the children are able to read and write using a range of words from Appendix List 1 in the NLS. Some children may be able to write sentences to compare the illustration and their own area, if they are given a simple writing frame such as:
- In the picture there is ...
- There is also ...
- In my town there is ...

You might find it useful to provide a list of vocabulary associated with places, buildings and street furniture, and which is relevant to the Geography curriculum. For example, see *A scheme of work for key stages 1 and 2 Geography*, Unit 1 Around our school – the local area, published by the QCA, or other Geography books (see 'Resources').

Resources

AS 'Sam's place'; a list of appropriate vocabulary; *Folens Geography Big Book Ages 6–7*

Sam's place

Name: .... **Date:** ....

This is where Sam lives. Read all about it.

1. What town does Sam live in?
2. Where does he go to school?
3. Where does he go swimming?
4. Where would Sam buy food for his dog?
5. Label the four shops in the High Street.
6. Circle where Sam lives.
7. Now write one question about Sam's town to ask a friend.

　　　　　　MAE1

Vocabulary extension

Learning objectives

Word level
- *To collect new words from reading and shared experiences, and to make collections of ... significant words.*
- To identify synonyms.

Activity sheet/Expectations

By this stage, the children should already have a sufficiently good vocabulary to recognise that certain words have the same or similar meanings. The activity sheet can be used to point out that writing can be made more interesting by having a range of words from which to choose. Some of the words on the cards are themselves similar, such as *frost/cold* and *storm/wind*, but the children should try to decide which of the words at the bottom of the sheet are the best match. The children should also understand that some words may be more appropriate than others in a given context. (For example, *warm/heated: It is a warm day* but *The water in the swimming pool is warm/The water in the swimming pool is heated*.)

You may find it useful if the children work in pairs to discuss possible meanings. The synonyms can be classified as follows:

size
large/huge
small/tiny

temperature
cold/chilly
warm/heated

weather
wet/rainy
fog/mist
wind/breeze
storm/hurricane
frost/ice

action
jump/leap

Further activities

Ask the children to find other synonyms that might also match the words on the activity sheet, depending on context. (For example, *warm/heated/stuffy* or *warm/sunny/bright*.) They can then think of sentences in which they could use the words.

You can discuss further the way we use some synonyms in precise contexts. (For example, *I will have my hair cut short* but *It will be a short holiday/It will be a brief holiday*.)

The children can decide if their own collections of personal interest words have synonyms that they could use in their writing.

The game of 'Snap!' can also be played using the synonyms on the activity sheets. It is a useful way to reinforce meaning. Other words can be added to the pack at a later date.

Resources

AS 'Make a pair'; simple dictionaries and thesauruses

Make a pair

Name: .... **Date:** ....

1. Read the cards.

2. Match these words to the cards. Write the matching word below its picture.

leap   rainy   huge   tiny   ice   mist   chilly
breeze   heated   hurricane

Topic words 1

Learning objectives

Word level
- *To collect new words from reading and shared experiences, and to make collections of words ... linked to particular topics.*
- To classify words under headings.

Activity sheet/Expectations

This unit can be used in conjunction with the next, 'Topic words 2'. Here, all the words on the activity sheet come from topic words related to general knowledge or the curriculum. To carry out the tasks successfully, the children will need to have acquired some reading experience and an awareness of information outside their immediate world. They will have gained this in a variety of ways and through different media, such as television or perhaps ICT, as well as through books and discussion. Consequently they are likely to have a broad vocabulary for their age.

The children should also be able to classify words in suitable ways, and be able to form their letters sufficiently well to complete the table on the activity sheet.

The words can be grouped as follows:
Furniture: cupboard, bed, drawers, desk
Computer: mouse, CD, screen, keyboard
The Planets: Mars, Saturn, Sun, Jupiter
The World: sea, map, island, country

Further activities

Point to the use of capital letters for names and abbreviations. You can compare *Sun/sun* and the different contexts in which they occur.

You might also discuss the contents of the picture further with the children, comparing it with their own room.

You may then wish to introduce the children to simple picture dictionaries, glossaries and encyclopedias (see 'Resources'). Some pupils, depending on their development, may be able to find their way around these – but whether or not they can, it is useful to introduce them to the idea that words can be ordered or subjects classified.

Resources

AS 'Lucy's den'; *Folens Picture Dictionary* and *Folens Thematic Dictionary* (these are combined in one volume and the latter groups words and pictures under several common themes, such as the weather, numbers, colours, and so on)

Lucy's den

Name: .... Date: ....

1. This is Lucy's den. Look at the things she has.

2. Read these headings. They are all about Lucy's den.

Furniture	Computer	The Planets	The World

3. Write these words under the best headings. Look at the picture to help you.

> sea   mouse   Mars   cupboard   CD   screen   bed   Saturn
> drawers   keyboard   map   Sun   island   Jupiter   desk   country

MAE1

Topic words 2

Learning objectives

Word level
- *To collect new words from reading and shared experiences, and to make collections of words ... linked to particular topics.*
- To classify words under themes.

Activity sheet/Expectations

The activity sheet 'Think of a word!' is a simple board game, in which the player must think of words that can come under a classification or theme. A dice can be used to progress through the game (a six being thrown to start). There are sixteen squares in all, six of which are topic squares. These are: *wild animals*, *fruit*, *shapes*, *vegetables*, *birds* and *the seaside*. (It is assumed the children will know simple classifications such as: colours, pets and farm animals.) When a player lands his or her counter on a topic square, they must think of five words that are appropriate. (For example, under wild animals might come: lion, tiger, elephant, leopard and wolf.)

The game is sufficiently flexible to be used in a variety of ways:
- You can increase or decrease the number of words the children must think of when they land on a topic square.
- The game can be played alone or in pairs.
- If playing with a partner, the game can be competitive or collaborative. (For example, when a child lands on a topic square they can think of words alone or help each other, as appropriate. They can also take it in turns to record words, if required.)
- You can use the basic structure of the game and replace the topics with harder or easier categories.
- You can also replace the topics with those related to the current curriculum. (For example, topics in Geography, Mathematics, History or ICT.)
- The children can play the game several times. This means that they have to trawl for an ever-increasing number of words under each topic.

Further activities

Look up and discuss the children's choice of words with them, refining them as suitable. For example, if *snake* is chosen under wild animals, you might wish to introduce the word *reptile*.

The children could try to select suitable topics for the squares themselves. It is useful to see how far they can generalise and whether they have grasped that some words represent a class or type.

Resources

AS 'Think of a word!'; 1–6 dice; counters; *Folens Picture Dictionary* and *Folens Thematic Dictionary*

Think of a word!

Name: .... Date: ....

Identifying structures

Learning objectives

Sentence level
- *To begin using the term 'sentence' to identify sentences in text.*
- *To write ... sentences, and to reread, recognising whether or not they make sense, e.g. missing words, wrong order.*
- *To use full stops to demarcate sentences.*
- *To use a capital letter for the personal pronoun 'I' and for the start of a sentence.*

Activity sheet/Expectations

More able children may be using capital letters and full stops routinely in their writing, though they may be unaware of what a sentence is. They can, however, learn to recognise a sentence by difference, even if they are too young to define it – for example, by comparing them with onomatopoeic captions, such as those in the activity sheet illustrations. (The children may also have come across such captions in comics and stories.) You can point out that these captions are sounds, which correspond to the sound of actions.

Initially, the children are asked to read the text accompanying the illustrations, which is a mix of sentences and onomatopoeic expressions. Once this is done, the children are invited to provide sentences to accompany the expressions. They can be encouraged to include simple phrases to make their sentences more interesting. For example:
Whoosh! I am going down the slide.
Splash! I am splashing in the water.
Woof! I am barking as loud as I can.
Hi! I am waving to my friend.
Crash! We are bumping into each other.

(Please note the use of both the first person singular and plural.)

Finally, the children are asked to write their own sentences about the illustration. Some may wish to include onomatopoeia as well. Encourage them to read their completed work to a friend.

Further activities

The children will almost certainly have come across onomatopoeic expressions before, but may be unaware of the significance of the exclamation mark. If appropriate, point to these in the illustration.

Look for examples of onomatopoeia in comics. Let the children cut out and stick the cartoons in their books and add their own sentences.

Resources

AS 'Playtime'; comics

Playtime

What are these children doing? Look carefully at the picture.

1. Tick the sentences in the picture.

2. On the back of this sheet, write down those words that are not sentences, like this. *Fling!*

3. Add a sentence to your words in question 2, like this.
   Fling! I am throwing my ball in the air.

4. Write three new sentences about the picture.

Lines and sentences

Learning objectives

Sentence level
- *To recognise that a line of writing is not necessarily the same as a sentence.*
- To distinguish between a nursery rhyme and a story, and to compare and contrast.
- To work with simple formats, such as tick boxes.

Activity sheet/Expectations

Note: The nursery rhyme, 'There was a little girl', probably dates from the nineteenth century. It is commonly thought that Henry Wadsworth Longfellow wrote it when Edith, his daughter, was reluctant to have her hair curled (you might like to refer to *Popular Nursery Rhymes* or *An Alphabet of Rhymes*, as listed in 'Resources').

There is more than one task involved in the activity sheet, and these require the children to have developed simple organisational skills. They also need to be able to distinguish between prose and poetry, comparing several features of one with the other.

They are given a list of simple statements and asked to tick the appropriate boxes, according to whether or not they fit the features of a nursery rhyme or a story opening. Both examples fall into opposite categories. The fourth statement in each case, however, *This is writing*, applies to both. As the children work, you may wish to note, in particular, if the children can distinguish between a line of poetry and a sentence.

There is a considerable amount of text on the activity sheet and the children need to be confident readers, with a reading age of approximately seven to eight years, in order to tackle it effectively. Point to difficult vocabulary, such as *forehead*, *horrid* and *rhyme*.

You may feel it is useful for the children to work in suitable pairs and discuss the statements with each other to arrive at a consensus.

Further activities

The children can complete the story using the story opening on the activity sheet as a stimulus, again working either alone or in pairs. Some may be able to write three simple paragraphs, using the opening as the first paragraph. They can then provide the middle paragraph and a conclusion themselves.

You can also show the children, or ask them to find, simple questionnaires that use tick boxes. These are sometimes found in comics.

If suitable, point to the use of commas to separate adjectives in the story opening.

Resources

AS 'What can it be?'; *Popular Nursery Rhymes*, edited by Jennifer Mulherin (Granada); *An Alphabet of Rhymes* from *Folens Spelling Foundation File* (Folens); comics

What can it be?

Name: .... **Date:** ....

Read these two extracts. Answer the questions by ticking **Yes** or **No**.

There was a little girl,
And she had a little curl,
Right in the middle of her forehead.
When she was good,
She was very very good,
And when she was bad,
She was horrid!

	Yes	**No**
1. This is a rhyme.	☐	☐
2. This is the start of a story.	☐	☐
3. This is writing.	☐	☐
4. The words are in lines.	☐	☐
5. The words are in sentences.	☐	☐

Once upon a time there was a tiny boy.
He lived in a tiny tree house at the top
of a very tall tree. He wore a smart
green coat and a neat blue hat, but he
always muddled up his socks. One sock
was red and the other was yellow.

	Yes	**No**
1. This is a rhyme.	☐	☐
2. This is the start of a story.	☐	☐
3. This is writing.	☐	☐
4. The words are in lines.	☐	☐
5. The words are in sentences.	☐	☐

What happened to the tiny boy? Finish the story.

Spoken and written forms

Learning objectives

Text level
- *To notice the difference between spoken and written forms by telling stories; compare oral versions with the written text.*
- To tell own stories.
- To write own stories.

Activity sheet/Expectations

For this activity, the children will need to work in pairs to discuss what is happening in the illustration. The questions they are asked are:
How many animals can you find?
What are they doing?
How did they do it?
Where did they come from?

These questions should stimulate discussion and be used as a springboard for the children to tell each other stories. They will have to use their imaginations to decide how the animals got into the kitchen and how, for example, they stole the food. (There are various clues, such as open windows, a garden path, and so on.)

Once they have discussed what all the animals are doing, they can choose one as the focus for a story, and recount it to a partner, making it up as they go along.

Further activities

When the children have told their stories, they can form simple written versions, adding story structures, such as *Once upon a time*. They will need to select information from the oral version before deciding together which are the most interesting parts to include.

You can then discuss with them how oral story versions accommodate change and development more easily, and how a written text is fixed, requiring complex structures, such as sentences. It is useful to keep a selection of interesting pictures for discussion, especially those that are heavily detailed or have limited text. John Burningham's classic picture book, *The Seasons*, has pull-out illustrations (see 'Resources'). You may also like to use particular Victorian genre paintings, such as *The Railway Station* (see 'Resources').

The children can create their own pictures with 'hidden stories' and ask other children to develop these.

Resources

AS 'What are they up to?'; *The Seasons* by John Burningham (Jonathan Cape); *The Railway Station* painted by William Frith in 1862

What are they up to?

Talk about these questions with a partner.

● How many animals can you find?

● What are they doing?

● How did they do it?

● Where did they come from?

Now choose an animal each. Tell your partner a story about it.

Following instructions on a map

Learning objectives

Text level
- *To read and follow simple instructions* on a pictorial map.
- To read in sequence.
- To deduce information.

Activity sheet/Expectations

Here the children are presented with a pictorial map of an imaginary city farm. It is useful if they have already studied simple maps and have some concept of what a map is. They should also be able to distinguish between left and right.

There are several skills involved in the tasks. The children are expected to:
- follow the route around the farm sequentially;
- proceed along the route by following numbers and signs;
- read information and make deductions;
- record what they have deduced by listing information and using commas.

They can use a pen or pencil to mark the trail as they go. They can then follow the trail again to identify what is required in the questions, if they have not already done so. A few children may have sufficiently good organisational skills to be able to carry out both activities at once.

The following animals should be listed: lambs, pigs, chickens, ducks, donkeys, goats and geese. In addition, the animals in the pets' corner are: hamsters, mice and rabbits. A cat and her kittens and a dog and her puppies should also be noted.

The children might list vegetables and other farm produce in answer to question 3. Or, alternatively, they might list souvenirs. Again, make sure the children use commas when writing their lists.

Further activities

There are several other observations to be made about the map, which can be used as discussion points. For example:
- the geese are stealing the lettuces from the vegetable patch;
- one pig is rolling in the mud;
- the mother cat is cleaning a kitten;
- two ducks are splashing in the pond.

You can also link this work to other subjects, such as map skills in Geography. Some children may also have visited city farms. They can discuss their experiences and, where suitable, how these differ from rural farms.

Resources

AS 'Bramble Lane'; examples of simple maps (both real and pictorial)

Bramble Lane

Name: .... **Date:** ....

1. Look at this map of Bramble Lane City Farm. Follow the trail with a pencil.

2. Make a list of all the animals you can find at Bramble Lane. Don't forget to use commas in your list.

3. What things could you buy at the farm shop? Write a sentence, listing all the things. Again, remember to use commas!

MAE1

Labels

Learning objectives

Text level
- *To write and draw simple instructions and labels for everyday classroom use, e.g. in role-play area, for equipment.*
- To complete words by using contextual and grapheme/phoneme relationships.

Activity sheet/Expectations

On the activity sheet, 'Labels for Ravi', the children are asked to complete the words on labels that are common to infant classrooms. Although pictures are supplied as prompts, the children should be familiar with most of the words, even if they cannot spell them all correctly.

Labels in classrooms often include surprisingly complex structures, involving such features as polysyllabic words, vowel digraphs, double letters, soft and hard sounds, and so on. Several skills focusing on reading and writing are involved in the activity sheet and the children will need to recognise, for example:
- single words;
- initial sounds (*B* in *Books*);
- medial sounds (*ou* in *House*);
- word endings (*er* in *Rubbers*);
- plurals (*es* in *Brushes*);
- soft and hard sounds (soft *c* in *Pencils*, hard *c* in *Pictures*).

Once the work has been completed, the children can supply three labels (or more) which are pertinent to their own classrooms.

Further activities

Although many more able children have good visual recall – a particularly useful skill when spelling – some will not, so note the children's miscues and those skills they are using to spell words. Good phonic alternatives (such as *Pensils* rather than *Pencils*) indicates good progress, while bizarre spelling in an exceptionally able child (where the letter order bears little or no resemblance to the word) may indicate difficulties. (Please note, however, that such features as letter reversal, particularly *b* and *d*, may persist for some time, without there being any cause for concern.)

Ask the children to write labels for the classroom and captions for their own work for the classroom wall or work board.

Point to the use of capital letters for the initial letter of a word when writing labels.

Resources

AS 'Labels for Ravi'

Labels for Ravi

Name: .... Date: ....

1. Ravi is new to the class. He cannot find the things he needs because the labels are old and torn. Write the missing letters to help him.

Pe _ s

Pen _ _ _ _

Rul _ _ _

Rub _ _ _ _ _

Play h _ _ _ _

Bru _ _ _ _ _

Pi _ _ ures

_ _ int pots

_ ook_

_ ats and b _ _ _ _

_ and and sp _ _ _

2. Now write three more classroom labels on the back of this sheet.

Critical features of words

Learning objectives

Word level
- *To recognise the critical features of words, e.g. length ... and shape of letters.*

Text level
- *To use phonological, contextual, grammatical and graphic knowledge to work out, predict and check the meanings of unfamiliar words and to make sense of what they read.*
- To write simple notes, using stylistic conventions.

Activity sheet/Expectations

The activity sheet consists of a series of notes sent to a child by friends and members of her family. There are single words missing from each note, and the children must make the correct choice from a selection of three. The answers are: *come*, *pumped*, *sandwiches*, *feed*.

To do this effectively, they must discriminate between words by identifying the length and shape of the word. Patterns are given as an aid. However, the children may also need to use grammatical cues. For example, in the third note the words *sandwiches* and *chocolate* are similar in length and shape, but require different verb parts (that is, *Your sandwiches are ...* while *Your chocolate is ...*).

It is useful if the children use contextual and phonological cues to solve the puzzles, particularly when verifying choices, but most words can be identified graphically.

The children are then asked to write notes in reply. They should try to decide who the senders of the notes are and what relation they have to Josie, before writing their replies. For example, Polly could be a sister or a friend, while Billy is almost certainly a brother. Also encourage them to create interesting scenarios. For example, it may not be Josie's turn to feed the rabbit! In this way they will write more interesting replies.

Further activities

Ask the children to bring in different examples of 'note' writing, such as postcards, birthday cards or cards sent on special occasions (such as Diwali), emails, and so on. They can study the similarities and differences between these and the way notes are sent out, including the way in which they are addressed, topped and tailed.

Resources

AS 'Josie's notes'; holiday postcards, greetings cards, emails

Josie's notes

Name: .... **Date:** ....

1. Josie has received these notes, but some of the words are missing.
   Choose the best words and write them in.

Dear Josie

Can you [   ] swimming at 4pm?

from Polly

| come | go | be |

Look carefully
at the shape
of the words

Dear Josie

I have [   ] up the tyres on your bike.

love from Mum

| blown | pumped | let down |

Dear Josie

Your [   ] are in the fridge.

love Gran

| apples | sandwiches | chocolate |

Dear Josie

Can you [   ] the rabbit tonight?

from Billy

| feed | stroke | comb |

2. Now write notes from Josie back to Polly and Billy.

Word endings

Learning objectives

Word level
- *To investigate, read and spell words ending in ff, ll, ss, ck, ng, sh.*
- To investigate, read and spell words with medial ff, ll, ss, ck, ng, sh.
- To use rhyme to identify unknown words.

Text level
- *To use phonological, contextual and graphic knowledge to work out, predict and check the meanings of unfamiliar words and to make sense of what they read.*

Activity sheet/Expectations

In this activity sheet, the children are encouraged to use a variety of strategies to find some rhyming words. All the words contain the endings listed under the 'Learning objectives' above. The cues come from:
– rhyme;
– sentence and line context;
– grapheme/phoneme relationships.

Some of the words are tricky to rhyme but, providing the children select words that contain the appropriate word patterns, they can use their imaginations. The majority of the class are likely to think of the most obvious words, but others may not and may unwittingly include or repeat other sound patterns as shown in the example on the activity sheet.

Some further suggestions are given below and you may wish to discuss these with the children subsequently:
Shells like tinkling bells/spells/smells/wells.
Miss Snake makes a hiss/hissing/kiss/kissing sound.
Hickory, dickory dock, the mouse went up the clock/hid in the sock.
Splish went the washing/the dish/fish/wish.
Spring is singing/winging/swinging.

Further activities

Ask the children to identify or point to other sound patterns and rhymes such as: *snake/make*.

The following Caribbean rhyme is also useful for reinforcing *ck* sounds.
Ten biscuits in a pack,
Who don't want dem, turn their back.
Back to back, sago-pap,
Ten biscuits in a pack.

Resources

AS 'How many rhymes?'

How many rhymes?

Name: .... Date: ....

1. Read the lines below.

2. Say the words that are underlined. Write down a word that rhymes on the line.

3. Now write a list of as many rhyming words as you can.

<u>huff</u> → huff and puff

→ huff, puff, buff, chuff, gruff, ruff, stuff, snuff

<u>Shells</u> like tinkling..

....

<u>Miss</u> Snake makes a..

....

<u>Splish</u> went the..

....

Hickory, dickory <u>dock</u>, ...

....

<u>Spring</u> is..

....

Making sense

Learning objectives

Sentence level
- *To predict words from preceding words in sentences and investigate the sorts of words that 'fit'.*
- To identify questions in a passage and answer them by completing simple writing frames.

Activity sheet/Expectations

The activity sheet involves a non-fiction passage whose content should be within most children's experience. The readability level is approximately eight years and the children should be able to read the passage without hesitation, in order to complete the tasks.

They should read the passage through first before selecting the most appropriate words from the choice given. It is best if they work alone to complete the first and second questions, although they could work in pairs to discuss the third.

The children have to employ a variety of skills when reading the text. They have to:
- gain an overall understanding of the passage;
- deduce answers from preceding words;
- deduce answers from subsequent words (for instance, when selecting from *children/babies/people*);
- choose the best word from three possible answers (for example, when selecting from *towns/places/cities*);
- choose the correct word (for instance, when selecting from *cold/boiling/warm*);
- identify the questions in the passage.

The children are then asked to complete a simple writing frame, in order to give reasonable explanations. (For example, they are unlikely to know what a beekeeper's protective clothes are, but should be able to deduce why protective clothes would be needed.)

Note whether or not the children use difficult words from the passage to support their writing. For example:
I think a firefighter would wear a helmet and special clothes because these would protect them from the fire.

Note also that the conditional is used in the writing frame and whether or not the children use it, too.

Further activities

Having identified the children's areas of weakness, you may like to provide work that targets these, using similar passages. You might, for example, provide work that focuses on a difficulty in selecting the best from a series of words, all of which make sense in a passage.

Resources

AS 'All kinds of clothes'

All kinds of clothes

Name: .... **Date:** ....

1. Read this passage.

People who live in cold **towns/places/cities** wear lots of clothes to keep **cold/boiling/warm**. In hot and dry places like deserts, people wear long **shoes/clothes/raincoats**. This is to protect them from the **sun/moon/stars**.

Some **children/babies/people** wear special clothes for work. What kinds of clothes would a firefighter wear? What kinds of clothes would a beekeeper wear?

2. Read through 'All kinds of clothes' again. Circle the best word from the three in bold each time.

3. There are two questions in 'All kinds of clothes'. Find them, then answer them below.

I think a firefighter would wear _____

_____

_____

because _____

_____

_____

I think a beekeeper would wear _____

_____

_____

because _____

_____

Capital letters 1

Learning objectives

Sentence level
- *To continue demarcating sentences in writing, ending a sentence with a full stop.*
- *To use capital letters for the personal pronoun 'I' and for the start of a sentence.*

Activity sheet/Expectations

You may wish to use this activity sheet in conjunction with the activity sheet 'Capital letters 2' on page 50.

It is not uncommon for more able children to leave out full stops and capital letters in their writing, even when they know how to use them, as their thoughts run too far ahead of their writing skills.

The postcard on the activity sheet, though short, contains several mistakes involving full stops, capital letters for the beginning of sentences and for the pronoun *I*.

The children should read through the postcard first. They may need to do so several times, in order to make sense of it and to identify where the full stops should be placed, e.g. a full stop *after* 'yesterday' not *before*. It is best if they then complete that activity before dealing with capital letters.

There are 13 mistakes in all.

Dear Tom

I am having a wonderful time at the seaside. I have made sand pies and I made a castle too. I stuck shells all around it. We ate lots of ice cream yesterday. Ella was sick! We are coming home tomorrow.

I hope you are well.
from Harry

The children are asked to identify the nature of the mistakes, which should reinforce the correct patterns. (You can, for example, refer to the activity sheet and Harry's mistakes at a later date as a prompt for the children should you need to.)

Further activities

Point to the use of the capital letter in *Tom*, *Ella* and *Harry* and remind the children that capital letters are used for names. Point also to the capital *D* in *Dear*.

The use of the exclamation mark can also be noted. The children should understand that it replaces the full stop and is not added to it. Discuss also its function, if necessary.

You may like to use this in conjunction with the activity sheet 'Josie's notes' on page 25 to compare the layout and conventions of postcards and notes.

Resources

AS 'A postcard from Harry'

A postcard from Harry

Harry and Ella have been to the seaside. Harry has sent a postcard to Tom, but he kept making the same mistakes.

1. Read Harry's postcard until it makes sense to you.

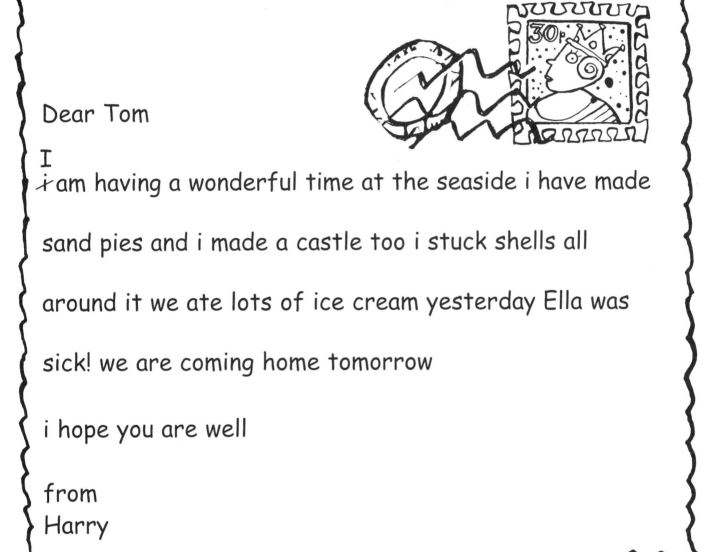

Dear Tom

I
~~i~~ am having a wonderful time at the seaside i have made

sand pies and i made a castle too i stuck shells all

around it we ate lots of ice cream yesterday Ella was

sick! we are coming home tomorrow

i hope you are well

from
Harry

What kinds of mistakes did Harry keep making?

2. Correct Harry's mistakes. The first one has been done for you.

Story elements

Learning objectives

Text level
- *To identify and compare basic story elements, e.g. beginnings and endings in different stories.*
- To identify traditional story openings.
- To use context cues.

Sentence level
- *To expect reading to make sense and check if it does not, and to read aloud using expression appropriate to the grammar of the text.*

Activity sheet/Expectations

The activity sheet consists of a series of story endings and beginnings for the children to identify. There are certain cues for them to spot, however, that signal which is which:
– all the story beginnings follow the traditional patterns of folk and fairy tales, such as *Once upon a time ...* or *Long ago ...*;
– all the endings have strong closure.

In order to complete the task, therefore, the children need to be experienced listeners and readers and familiar with these patterns.

Once all the beginnings and endings have been identified, the children can then match them up. Yet again, they will need to pick up cues in the texts. (In each case, the main character or characters are mentioned.)

The examples are matched as follows: A/C, B/F, D/H, G/E

Children can work in pairs to read the examples to each other. They can also encourage each other to make sense and read with expression. For example, they can contrast the tone of the voice in C with F.

Further activities

If the children are working in pairs, ask them each to choose a matched beginning and ending and make up a story. They can recount these tales to each other orally.

Alternatively, ask them to share the tasks so that they each contribute in turn to making the same story. This activity can also be carried out in a larger group.

Select different fairy stories, for example those by the brothers Grimm or Hans Christian Andersen, and encourage the children to compare different traditional story beginnings.

Resources

AS 'Beginnings and endings'; examples of traditional fairy stories; red and blue pens

Beginnings and endings

Name: .... **Date:** ....

1. Read these extracts.

A. Once upon a time there was a duck.

B. Far away on a distant island
there lived a mean troll.

C. The little duck put his head under
his wing and fell fast asleep.

D. There was once a pebble that lived by the seashore.

E. But the Moon would only come out
at night, whatever the Sun God did.

F. The troll stamped her foot and shouted.
She kicked the ground and screamed. But
it was no good. It was no good at all.

G. Long ago, before time began, there
was a great Sun God.

H. The pebble was tossed in the air by a
great wave. Higher and higher it
went, and further out to sea.

2. Tick all the **story beginnings** with a red pen.

3. Circle all the **story endings** with a blue pen.

4. Draw lines to match the beginnings with the right endings.

MAE1   33

Actions and rhymes

Learning objectives

Text level

- *To learn and recite simple poems and rhymes, with actions, and to reread them from the text.*
- *To substitute and extend patterns from reading through language play, e.g. by using same lines and introducing new words, ... adding further rhyming words.*

Activity sheet/Expectations

Christina's Rossetti's well-known poem, 'The pancake', can be committed to memory more easily and spoken with greater expression if the actions are included, and the children are asked to create their own actions for the poem. They can recite and act out the results to a partner or to other groups of children.

The poem in the second part of the activity, 'Cut the bread', reinforces the rhythm of 'The pancake', and this should help the children to complete the tasks. They should be encouraged to experiment when answering question 5, placing the lines differently as they choose. However, ultimately they should try to identify the lines with the rhyming words and pair them. For example:

Cut the bread,
Spread the butter,
Take a little bite.

Add some jam,
If you can,
Eat it as you like!

Further activities

You might give the children rhymes, such as *yum/tum/crumb*, and ask them to try and create their own lines for the poem, 'Cut the bread'. They might make lists of rhyming words. Begin, for example, with *lick* and make *brick, click, chick, slick*, and so on.

Ask the children to find other rhymes in the poem. For example, *bread/spread* and *jam/can*. Reinforce the idea that rhyming words do not have to be spelled in the same way, they only need sound the same or similar.

Some may be able to complete simple rhymes using their own words entirely. Give the following starter to the children and ask them to try:

Where's the pasta?
Here's the pasta,

_____

Resources

AS 'The pancake'

The pancake

Name: .... **Date:** ....

1. Read this poem by Christina Rossetti.

Mix a pancake,
Stir a pancake,
Pop it in the pan.

Fry the pancake,
Toss the pancake,
Catch it if you can.

2. Make up some actions to go with it.

3. Now read this poem. Some of the lines are missing.

Cut the bread,
Spread the butter,

_____ .

Add some jam,
If you can,

_____ !

4. Read the poem again and again, trying out these last lines.
Take a little bite/Eat it as you like
Take a little lick/Eat it quick, quick, quick

5. Write down the lines you like best in the gaps.

Alliteration

Learning objectives

Text level
- *To substitute and extend patterns from reading through language play, e.g. ... by alliterative patterns.*
- To identify alliteration.

Activity sheet/Expectations

Tongue twisters depend largely on alliteration for their effect. They are fun to read and a useful way to teach the technique of alliteration.

The tongue twister on the activity sheet is an extract from the poem 'Betty Botter'. Once the children have practised reading it, they could try the full version (the second verse is given below).

So she bought a bit of butter,
Better than her bitter butter,
And she put it in her batter,
And the batter was not bitter.
It was better Betty Botter bought a bit of better butter.

In the subsequent tasks the children are asked to identify other alliterative sounds. There is a subtle difference between some of these (for instance, *s*, *sh* and *sw*). Note whether or not the children identify them all as *s* or recognise the consonant digraph *sh* and the blend *sw*.

Further activities

Children are adept at creating sounds and nonsense patterns in their play. They can use these skills to good effect when making tongue twisters. For example, they can create lines or couplets with words linked by sounds, such as those included on the activity sheet. Begin with the double *tt* words from the poem and ask the children to make as many more as they can, for example: *butter, bitter, batter, better, patter, pitter, fatter, fitter*, and so on. They might make these into tongue twisters. You might also look at some examples of other tongue twisters with the children for ideas (see 'Resources').

They can think of their own words or you could provide word lists for them. (These are sometimes found at the back of simple dictionaries.)

Resources

AS 'Betty Botter'; examples of tongue twisters, such as *Teasing Tongue Twisters*, poems selected by John Foster (Collins); *Tongue Twisters and Tonsil Twizzlers*, poems chosen by Paul Cookson (Macmillan)

Betty Botter

Name: .... **Date:** ....

1. Try to read this rhyme.

Betty Botter bought some butter,
"But," she said, "the butter's bitter.
If I put it in my batter,
It will make my batter bitter,
But a bit of better butter,
Will make my batter better."

2. Now read it again quickly!

3. Circle the letter that starts lots of words in Betty Botter.

d   m   e   l   n   b   p

4. Now do the same for these words.

silk and satin

t   r   l   p   sh   f   sw   s

post a poem

t   r   l   p   sh   f   sw   s

terrible tears and tantrums

t   r   l   p   sh   f   sw   s

shadows shake

t   r   l   p   sh   f   sw   s

swallows sweep

t   r   l   p   sh   f   sw   s

5. Make up your own words that begin with these letters.

r   m   l

Developing a story

Learning objectives

Text level
- *To represent outlines of story plots using, e.g. captions, pictures ... to make a wall story of own version.*

Activity sheet/Expectations

It is assumed the children can sequence and have a sound understanding of the linear progress of a traditional story: beginning, middle and end. The activity sheet presents the children with:
- a story opening using pictures and captions, followed by;
- pictures only, to which the children must add the text, followed by;
- blank boxes, in which the children must draw the pictures and provide the text.

The activity sheet can therefore be used to complete the story by writing the middle and end.

The implication in pictures 3 and 4 is that someone – possibly a relation of Midge's – will eat the sugar mouse, and the real challenge for the children will be how to provide a resolution. (This could, for example, take the form of some kind of retribution, or the mouse might be saved from its fate.)

The children could work in pairs to discuss the story, as you prefer.

Further activities

Ask the children to develop the captions they have written into a fuller story using more complex sentences. For example, you could show them how the first caption can be developed into more interesting sentences:

There was once a mouse. He had pink ears, *a pink snout, a little pink wriggly tail, and he was made of sugar.*

Show the children how they would need to take out words as well as add them. They can then develop their sentences into paragraphs and follow the basic structure of a story with a beginning, middle and end.

You might also give them some simple stories in a range of tales at different levels – easy, intermediate and advanced – to cut up to create little books (see 'Resources'). Or, alternatively, they can produce a frieze or wall story and use the captions to sequence the story orally, embellishing the account as they go.

You can also point out and discuss with the children the differences between the written and oral versions.

Resources

AS 'The sugar mouse'; *World of Story* (Belair Publications)

The sugar mouse

Name: .... **Date:** ....

Read the start of this story. Then complete the pictures and captions.

1	**2**
There was once a mouse. He had pink ears and a pink snout, and he was made of sugar.	He belonged to Midge, who was six. Midge loved his pink sugar mouse. He would never eat him.
3	**4**
5	**6**

Building character

Learning objectives

Text level
- *To build simple profiles of characters from stories read, describing characteristics, appearances, behaviour with pictures, single words, captions, words and sentences from text.*
- To write a paragraph describing a character.

Activity sheet/Expectations

In this activity, the children are asked to build a character profile of a naughty girl, and then use it to write a simple character study in six sentences.

They are given a name and a brief description at the top of the sheet, which should help to suggest the image of a character in their minds. Help them to think how they might make their character *look* naughty, for example, the children can include: hair colour, distinguishing features (such as glasses), scornful expression, untidy clothes, torn school bag, and so on. They might also like to include a pet, such as a dog. The children can work alone or in pairs to construct the character, as you see fit.

Once the profile is complete, they are then asked to add information about the character. This can be written in the form of simple notes. No help is given, but the children should add comments such as: *screams and shouts, won't eat her dinner, takes others' sweets, doesn't do her work, always late for school, loses her bag, gets home late*, and so on.

You may wish to discuss these, and other points, before the children begin, depending on their ability. You might also wish to refer to similar characters in books or in films that the children already know and supply some suitable words.

Further activities

The children might look at pictures of characters from favourite books and comics. How do they *look* naughty? They should consider whether Minnie should be given any redeeming features, such as being kind to animals, small children or elderly people.

The character profiles can also be used as an impetus for a story about how the character changes. The children can talk about why and how this might happen. You might find it useful to have available a series of story books covering a range of characters, for example those by Beatrix Potter (see 'Resources').

Resources

AS 'Minnie'; colouring pens and pencils; children's storybooks; *Beatrix Potter* books (Frederick Warne); comics

Minnie

Name: .... **Date:** ....

Minnie was naughty. She was very naughty. She was one of the naughtiest girls in the world!

1. What do you think Minnie looks like? Draw a picture of her below.

2. Add words to say what she is like. Think of all the naughty things she would do.

3. Now write six sentences about Minnie.

_____

_____

_____

_____

_____

_____

Non-fiction books

Learning objectives

Text level
- *To read non-fiction books and understand that the reader doesn't need to go from start to finish but selects according to what is needed.*
- *To predict what a given book might be about from a brief look at both front and back covers, including blurb, title, illustration; to discuss what it might tell in advance of reading and check to see if it does.*

Activity sheet/Expectations

The activity sheet presents the children with information about an imaginary non-fiction book on toys that work. It includes the back and front covers, giving a brief blurb and details about the author and illustrator. Most information is explicit, although the title does not indicate that the book deals with specific kinds of toys and the children must try to deduce this.

The activity sheet also includes examples of typical inside pages with non-consecutive page numbers. This is to reinforce the idea that a non-fiction book can be dipped into for information. In addition, the pages only have illustrations, both to reinforce the concept of 'toys that work' and also the idea that we can identify immediately whether or not the page will be useful to us.

The children should write down their answers on the sheet. Note in particular who has difficulty with question 5. Discuss how the title might be changed to make the book's content clearer.

Further activities

Give the children a range of non-fiction books (including reference books, as well as information books and picture books) that vary in complexity, so that they can study the front and back covers. The children can work in suitable groups or pairs taking it in turns to select randomly from a book box. They can then explain to each other what the books are about. To formalise the activity, you can, if you wish, draw up a checklist of details the children should cover, according to their ability level. For example:
- what kind of book is it? (Is it a dictionary, a book about flight, a picture book on the seasons with little text?)
- who is the author? Who is the illustrator?
- who would the book appeal to? (For example, would it be an older child, a younger child, someone who knew little about the subject, someone who knew a lot about the subject?)

The children can then discuss their opinions, agreeing and disagreeing with each other and, if possible, try to reach a shared view.

Resources

AS 'Looking at books'; a range of non-fiction and reference books

Looking at books

Name: .... Date: ....

1. Look at these book covers. Which is the front cover? Which is the
back cover?

2. Write down the title of the book ....

3. Who is the author? ....

4. Who drew the pictures? ....

5. Look at the pictures on the front cover again. What kind of things
would you find in the book? ....

6. Look at these pages from the book. What numbers are they?

7. Which page would you look at to find out about puppets? ....

8. What kind of puppets are they? ....

9. What are these pages about?

page 8 ....

page 3 ....

page 16 ....

Spelling patterns

Learning objectives

Word level
- *To recognise words by common spelling patterns.*
- To learn the pattern '-tch'.
- To learn the pattern '-dge'.

Activity sheet/Expectations

Children who have good visual and auditory skills can usually recall letter patterns easily, once alerted to them, and depend less on learning spelling rules to help them remember spellings. They may even find rules cumbersome. Others may find rules useful. (See below under 'Further activities'.)

The activity sheet focuses on the letter patterns *-tch* and *-dge*. The children are asked to identify the correct words from pictures. They are also given the initial letter of the word to help them. The children should be making good progress in spelling and should also have a sound vocabulary.

They are then asked to classify the words correctly on a table. Organisational skills should, therefore, also be sound. There are sixteen words in all. Listed correctly they are:

-tch	-dge
watch	badge
hutch	fudge
kitchen	bridge
pitch	hedge
ditch	judge
butcher	fridge
hatch	ledge
patch	smudge

Further activities

To distinguish between the patterns *-ge* and *-dge*, the general rule is that after a short vowel, *d* comes before *ge*, while after a long vowel, there is no *d* (for example, *page*, *stage*, *cage*). However, there are exceptions in polysyllabic words (for example, *village*, *cottage*).

The letter pattern *-tch* can be viewed similarly. Again, there are exceptions, and not only in polysyllabic words (for example, *much*, *such*, *which*, *sandwich*, *ostrich*).

Note: Using a spelling programme can help to clarify some spelling rules.

Resources

AS 'Badger's catch'; *Folens Spelling Programme*, Files 1, 2 and 3

Badger's catch

Badger has been catching words. What has she caught?

1. Say the names of the things below. Look at the first letter to help.
(Some have been done to help you.)

w   b   h   f

k   pitch   b   h

ditch   b   j   f

h   l   p   smudge

2. Now list Badger's words under the correct heading, like this.

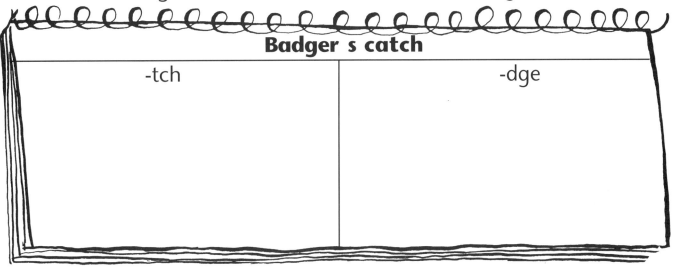

Badger s catch	
-tch	-dge

Past tense endings

Learning objectives

Word level
● *To investigate and learn spellings of verbs with '-ed' (past tense) and other changes.*

Activity sheet/Expectations

The game on the activity sheet 'Change the word!' uses the same structure as the game 'Think of a word!' on page 13 but is more difficult since it involves spelling and recording. The children are asked to turn verbs from the present to the past tense using -*ed*, -*d*, -*t* and -*ed* (preceded by a double consonant) and by making irregular changes.

The rules and procedure of the game are also more difficult, since the children have to write down their answers and check them as they go. The game can be played alone or in pairs:
1. A six should be thrown to decide who starts. (If a one is subsequently thrown, a player must begin on the first square.)
2. When a player lands his or her counter on a square, they must turn the verb from the present to the past tense.
3. A round finishes when the last square is reached. The exact number must be thrown to finish.

The children will need to record their words without others seeing. If you wish, the game can be played collaboratively or in two pairs, so that the children decide on the answers together. In addition, more than one round can be played. The children should retain their lists of words and record only new ones.

In order to play the game effectively, the children need to have good reading experience and should be forming grammatical structures accurately. (For example, *I found* not *finded*).

The answers are: walked, heard, climbed, held, skipped, crept, said, hopped, found, patted.

Further activities

You can note which verbs the children have difficulty with and address these specifically. Once the children are sufficiently familiar with the verbs, you could replace them. For example: *feel, bore, store, keep, mend, live, call, do, go, swim.*

You could also ask children to play a simpler version of the game in which they say the past tense of the verbs, rather than spell them. This approach is useful for those children who have difficulty in formulating word structures correctly and will help you to identify particular areas of weakness.

Resources

AS 'Change the word!'; 1–6 dice; counters

Change the word!

Name: .... Date: ....

1	**2**	**3** walk	**4** hear
5 climb	**6** hold	**7**	**8** skip
9	**10** creep	**11** say	**12** hop
13 find	**14**	**15** pat	**16**

Present tense endings

Learning objectives

Word level
- *To investigate and learn spellings of verbs with ... '-ing' (present tense) endings.*
- To spell correctly changes to verbs with a silent 'e', in which the 'e' is dropped when adding '-ing' (e.g. live/living).
- To spell correctly verbs in which the consonant is doubled before adding '-ing' (e.g. hop/hopping).

Activity sheet/Expectations

The children should be aware that *-ing* can be added to a verb, and they will often use it to write in the present tense. However, they may be less familiar with the way in which the initial verb structure changes in certain words. Once alerted they should be capable of spelling these correctly.

The activity sheet depicts a swimming pool with a series of activities going on that the children should identify. They will sometimes need to add *-ing* and at other times alter the original verb as follows:

Adding -ing: *jump/jumping, splash/splashing, throw/throwing, catch/catching, climb/climbing;*
Dropping the silent *e*: *dive/diving, wave/waving, smile/smiling;*
Doubling the consonant before adding *-ing*: *swim/swimming, run/running, sit/sitting.*

Further activities

The children are likely to identify those verbs especially linked to the illustration (such as *swimming, diving, waving* and *splashing*) and should therefore cover a range of spelling patterns. If necessary, point to other activities and ask them to supply the verbs. Also note any additional verbs they identify and any spelling patterns with which the children experience difficulty. The children should compare notes to find any *-ing* words they have missed.

The children could then write one or two paragraphs about the picture using the words they have made.

Ask the children to provide the past tense of the verbs, noting regular and irregular patterns (as in *swim/swimming/swam*).

Resources

AS 'At the pool'

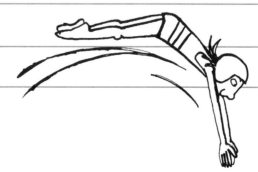

At the pool

Name: .... **Date:** ....

1. Look at the picture below.

2. Write down all the things the children are doing.
Write words with *-ing* endings like *chatting*. Think of twelve words
or more.

Capital letters 2

Learning objectives

Sentence level
- *To recognise other common uses of capitalisation, e.g. for personal titles (Mr, Miss, Mrs, Dr) ... book titles.*
- To use capital letters for names.

Activity sheet/Expectations

It is assumed the children will have some knowledge of using capital letters in a variety of contexts. In this activity, the focus is on capital letters for names and accompanying titles, and the titles of books, but the children are asked to incorporate their skills into other tasks. They are asked to:
– choose names for the child and adult characters, together with appropriate titles, as needed;
– match the books to the characters;
– complete sentences using capital letters for names and titles.

The children should select *Mr* and *Dr* for the baker and doctor, but the woman in the garden can be given any of the titles *Ms*, *Miss* or *Mrs*, as the children prefer.

In question 3, they should use the clues in the pictures to match the characters in the books as follows:
Toddler with teddy bear/*The Three Bears*
Boy with kitten/*Looking After Cats*
Girl with dog/ *My Dog Jock*
Baker/*Food, Food and More Food*
Doctor/*First Aid*
Gardener/*My Garden*

Ask the children to write their sentences on separate paper accurately, reminding them to use appropriate capital letters for names and titles, and also for the beginning of sentences.

Further activities

Ask the children to note examples of names and the use of capital letters in their immediate environment, such as names on shop fronts.

Use reference books (see 'Resources') to point to the use of capital letters for names and titles. You might also locate names and titles from the pages of newspapers or telephone directories. Make sure the children understand what each relates to, for example, *Rev* or *Dr*. When might you call someone *Sister* something or *Major* something?

If necessary, explain that place names have capital letters and give the children practice in identifying these. For example, by noting their addresses, the address of their school and names of places on maps.

Resources

AS 'Names'; telephone directories; maps such as an A–Z or a road atlas; non-fiction reference books

Names

1. Give each child a first name and write it down.

2. Give each adult a last name and a title and write them down.

3. Which book might each person in questions 1 and 2 like?

Write sentences to explain why you chose each book.

Sequencing and writing stories

Learning objectives

Text level
- *To retell stories, to give the main points in sequence and to pick out significant incidents.*

Activity sheet/Expectations

In this activity, the children are given a muddled story sequence told in cartoon form, which they must sequence correctly. They are then asked to use the pictures as a structure for writing the story. (If you prefer, the children can cut out the pictures and put them in order.) Once this has been done properly, they can number the pictures on the back for future reference. There are some speech balloons included to help the children.

The pictures tell the tale of a child who does not want to have her hair cut and whose lack of cooperation ends up in a very odd hairstyle. The order of the pictures on the activity sheet is: 4, 2, 5, 3, 1

The children are also asked to consider which part of the story they like best. This can lead on to a discussion of the important moments in the story (such as the last picture, which is a comic resolution).

As far as possible, the children should try to write the stories unaided, referring only to the pictures. However, a writing frame to start the story might be given for those who need help. The name can be altered as each child sees fit. For example:

> *There was once a girl called Mandy.*
> *She had*
> *Her mum*
> *but Mandy*

Further activities

The children should read their completed stories to each other in a group and discuss different aspects of the plot. They can also discuss the similarities and differences between their stories.

Show the children how they can use adjectives to embellish their descriptions. For example, *There was once a girl called Mandy. She had very long, untidy hair.*

Resources

AS 'Tell me a story'

Tell me a story

Name: .... **Date:** ....

1. Put these pictures in the right order. Number them 1 to 5.

2. On spare paper, write the story in your own words. Use the pictures to help you divide your story into paragraphs. Cut out the pictures and use them to illustrate your story. Give your story a title.

Contrasting settings

Learning objectives

Text level
- *To compare and contrast stories with a variety of settings, e.g. space, imaginary lands, animal homes.*
- To identify story elements: settings, and characters.
- To anticipate what might happen in a story.

Activity sheet/Expectations

There are three descriptions on the activity sheet which, although different in content, share several features:
- they are all settings;
- they are all story openings;
- they all suggest a potential plot.

Initially, however, the children are asked to focus on the differences between the descriptions by identifying their particular characteristics. These relate to setting and character and the children must tick appropriate boxes. They should therefore be experienced in working with simple tables or grids. The grid should read as follows:

	A	B	C
space			✓
hedgehog		✓	
mountain	✓		
dragon	✓		
deserts			✓
cave	✓		
pond		✓	
planet			✓
leaves		✓	
sun			✓
friends	✓		
garden		✓	

A reading age of between eight and nine years is needed to read the passages confidently.

Further activities

The children can choose a setting as an opening, which they can develop into a story. They might like to make a plan first, either by using a writing frame or by creating a storyboard. It may also be useful if they discussed with other children potential plots first.

Note: See the previous activity sheet, 'Tell me a story', as a guide to creating a storyboard.

Resources

AS 'What's in the story?'

What's in the story?

Name: .... **Date:** ....

1. Read the passages A, B and C.

A

High on a mountain in a far off land, in a beautiful cave, lived a dragon.
The walls were covered with jewels that twinkled. The floor was covered
with velvet cloth. But the dragon was not happy because he had no friends.

B

There was once a garden. It was very large and it had a pond and apple
trees. At the bottom of the garden, where all the rubbish was kept, there
lived a hedgehog. He lived under a pile of old leaves. It was not a big pile and the
leaves were not the best leaves, but spring was just around the corner.

C

Far out in space, way beyond the sun, was an unknown planet. It was
covered in green dust that blew across green deserts. It had large
rocky cliffs and a green sea and it was about to be discovered.

2. Tick the boxes to match the words to the stories. The first has been
done for you.

	A	B	C
space			✓
hedgehog			
mountain			
dragon			
deserts			
cave			
pond			
planet			
leaves			
sun			
friends			
garden			

Poetry with similar themes 1

Learning objectives

Text level
- *To read a variety of poems on similar themes, e.g. pets.*
- *To compose own poetic sentences, using repetitive patterns, carefully selected sentences and imagery.*
- To pair words that rhyme.

Activity sheet/Expectations

This activity sheet can be used alone or in conjunction with the next unit, 'Poetry with similar themes 2'.

Although the charming little poem on the activity sheet should be within the reading ability of the children, it has three verses. It is better, therefore, if they have an audience to read to. They could work in suitable pairs, reading the poem a verse at a time to each other.

Completing the activity sheet requires the children to have good organisational skills as well as being able to recognise rhyme. In task 3, for example, the children could continue to work together. They will need to go through the rhyming words systematically, pairing them off, before they begin to complete the poems. They can then test their words out with each other as well as read the poems together.

The rhyming words are: *Fred/bed, strong/long, chew/shoe.*

The children are also asked to write their own poem about a real or imaginary pet. This can be done in several ways. They can use the structures available on the activity sheet, such as the repeating line *I have a ...* and *His/Her name is ...*, but it is difficult to find rhymes which are not forced and where the meaning does not suffer. It may also be difficult to find suitable rhymes for certain names.

Further activities

The children could try to write simple word pictures that suit their pets. They can think of typical situations (such as a cat curled up on a chair) and try to find similes. They can use the line *My cat/dog is like ...*, and repeat it for each new situation. Those that have unusual pets may be able to think of unusual similes.

Note: You might like to refer to the activity sheets 'The pancake' (page 35) and 'Betty Botter' (page 37) in this book for other familiar themes in poetry and rhyme.

Resources

AS 'My doggie'

My doggie

Name: ....   **Date:** ....

1. Read this poem by C Nurton.

I have a dog,
His name is Jack,
His coat is white
With spots of black.

I take him out,
Most every day,
Such fun we have,
We run and play.

Such clever tricks,
My dog can do,
I love my Jack,
He loves me too.

2. Finish these poems about other pets. Choose the correct rhyming
words from the box below.

green   Fred   shoe   strong   fox   many   chew   long   bed   Jamie

I have a fish,
His name is _____,
He sleeps near me,
Beside my _____.

I have a rabbit,
He likes to _____,
He ate Mum's glove,
And Dad's old _____.

I have a cat,
Her claws are _____,
Her fur is soft,
Her tail is _____.

3. Now write your own poem about a real or imaginary pet.

Poetry with similar themes 2

Learning objectives

Text level
- *To read a variety of poems on similar themes, e.g.* pets.
- *To compare and contrast ... common themes in ... poems.*
- *To collect class and individual favourite poems for class anthologies, participate in reading aloud.*
- To learn poems or parts of poems by heart.

Activity sheet/Expectations

This activity sheet can be used in conjunction with the previous one, 'Poetry with similar themes 1'.

The activity sheet can be used in several ways. It contains a single poem, which can be:
– read alone or in pairs;
– compared with the poem, 'My doggie', on the previous sheet;
– learned by heart, according to the children's interest and ability.

It is suggested that the children work with a partner and recite the poem to each other, either by taking turns or by reading a verse each. It is longer than the previous poem, 'My doggie', but has a similar rolling beat which is pleasurable and easy to recall. It also helps the children to commit the words to memory. The children can learn the whole poem or the first verse, as you see fit.

They should discuss the poem with each other and develop a mental picture of Spot. Familiarity will also help the children to compare the two poems. You can provide them with a table (or show them how to make one) in which simple notes are recorded. These might only be single words. For example:

'My doggie' and 'My dog, Spot':	The same	Different
	dogs	
	spots	names

The important point is that the children should be able to use their notes to explain the similarities and differences. They can do this to each other, to a wider group of children or to you. Early experience of reading notes back is also useful for future note-taking.

There are further similarities and differences between the poems that the children might note or that you can point out. For example, the similarities are that both dogs are clever, both dogs are loved and both like to play; the differences are that Spot doesn't like cats.

Further activities

Discuss the second verse of 'My dog, Spot' with the children pointing to the image of the dog thinking *When the weather is hot*. If the children enjoy the poems, they might like to add them to a collection of favourite animal poems.

Resources

AS 'My dog, Spot'

My dog, Spot

Name: .... **Date:** ....

Work with a partner to read this poem by Rodney Bennett.
Talk about what Spot looks like.

I have a white dog
Whose name is Spot,
And he's sometimes white
And he's sometimes not,
There's a patch on his ear
That makes him Spot.

He has a tongue
That is long and pink,
And he lolls it out
When he wants to think,
He seems to think most
When the weather is hot.
He's a wise sort of dog,
Is my dog, Spot.

He likes a bone
And he likes a ball,
But he doesn't care
For a cat at all.
He waggles his tail
And he knows what's what,
So I'm glad that he's my dog,
My dog, Spot.

Locating and recounting

Learning objectives

Text level
- *To identify simple questions and use text to find answers.*
- *To locate parts of text that give particular information including labelled pictures.*
- *To write simple recounts linked to topics of interest/study or to personal experience, using the language of texts read as models for own writing.*
- To write own account in the past tense.

Activity sheet/Expectations

In this activity, the children are asked to study an illustration of an adventure park, together with names and labels, and use the information to complete an account written by an imaginary child.

Since the account is begun in the past tense and is a recount of an experience, the children will need to continue in this tense and style (rather than describing the picture in the present tense). They should try to imagine themselves as Leroy in order to recount what has happened.

They also need to pick up certain cues by reading the labels in the picture. Leroy's friends, for example, are all given names. The children must then marry this information with what the character is doing so they can write their sentences. (There are also various anomalies in the picture, which the children are not required to note here, though some may pick these up and may also wish to include them in their writing. They are discussed below.)

Further activities

The children can add a conclusion to their account, describing the return journey using connectives. For example:

At four o'clock we all lined up. **Then** *we got on the coach. We saw all sorts of things on the way home. We saw …* **When** *we arrived at school, my mum was waiting to take me home.*

The illustration of Hilltop Park also contains various anomalies:
- Sue is feeding the ducks but there is a notice saying *Do not feed the ducks*;
- Ben is jumping in the lake but there is a notice saying *No swimming* and there is also a swimming pool available;
- Amy has thrown litter on the ground despite there being a litter bin.

These points can become the focus of discussion and you can also show the children how to extend their sentences using connectives. For example:

Sue fed the ducks **although** *there was a notice saying 'Do not feed the ducks'.*

Resources

AS 'Leroy's trip'

Leroy's trip

Name: .... **Date:** ....

Last week my class went on a school trip to Hilltop Park. We had lots of fun.

1. Read Leroy's account. Who are his friends? Write their names on the back of this sheet. What are they doing?

2. Finish Leroy's writing about his school trip. Say what his friends are doing, like this. *Sue fed the ducks.*

Non-fiction texts

Learning objectives

Text level
- *To use the language and features of non-fiction texts, e.g. labelled diagrams, captions for pictures.*
- *To weigh up the advantages and disadvantages of a topic and write down comments.*
- To use non-fiction information to write a paragraph.

Activity sheet/Expectations

The focus in this activity is to collect together simple information and present it in a non-fiction form, through such typical features as captions, labels and simple notes.

Once completed, the children should use the information to write a paragraph about the topic. It will be challenging for them to bring all the information together and write sentences, and you may wish to provide an example of how to do it. (See also the writing frame below under 'Further activities'.)

Initially, the children are asked to provide simple captions of a few words (not sentences) under the pictures. They are then asked to label an illustration of a car.

Some children will be better informed than others and may, for example, wish to include information about their favourite cars. They may also label the car differently. However, most children should already be aware of such issues as pollution, about which they are encouraged to express an opinion. (See illustration 1.)

Most children will also include the following additional labels: bonnet, headlight, roof, boot, door, wheels, mirrors.

Make available a range of simple books about the topic, which the children can use to find out more information. Some may be able to include this in their accounts.

Further activities

Ask the children to use the work they have done to write a paragraph of six sentences about the car. They should try to express an opinion. You could use the following writing frame:

There are some good things about cars. First of all ...

and

There are also some bad things about cars. I think ...

I also think ...

Resources

AS 'On the road'; simple books about cars

On the road

Name: .... **Date:** ....

1. Write some words under each of these pictures. The first has been done for you.

Going fast!

2. Label the picture with these words:

tyre   engine   windscreen

3. Now think of five more labels and add them. Use arrows to show what you are labelling.

4. Write down three good things about cars. Write down three bad things about cars.

Good things	Bad things

      MAE1

Objectives grid

	Word	Page	Sentence	Page	Text	Page
T1	Rhyme	4	Writing captions and simple sentences	6	Reciting stories and rhyme	4
	Read familiar words	6	Beginning to use the term 'sentence'	14	Noticing the difference between spoken and written forms	18
	Collect new words	8, 10, 12	Writing and rereading sentences	14	Telling own stories	18
	Synonyms	8	Using full stops	14	Writing own stories	18
	Classify words	10, 12	Using capital letters	14	Reading and following simple instructions	20
					Reading in sequence	20
			Recognising that a line of writing is not always a sentence	16		
			Distinguishing between nursery rhymes and stories	16	Deducing information	20
			Working with simple formats	16	Writing and drawing simple instructions and labels	22
					Complete words	22
T2	Critical features of words	24	Predicting words	28	Using phonological, contextual, grammatical and graphic knowledge	24, 26
	Words ending: ff, ll, ss, ck, ng, sh	26	Identifying questions	28	Writing simple notes	24
	Words with the medial: ff, ll, ss, ck, ng, sh	26			Identifying basic story elements	32
	Rhyme	26	Using capital letters	30	Identifying story openings	32
			Expecting reading to make sense	32	Using context cues	32
					Learning and reciting simple poems	34
					Substituting and extending patterns from reading	34, 36
					Identifying alliteration	36
					Representing outlines of story plots	38
					Building character profiles	40
					Writing character paragraphs	40
					Reading non-fiction books	42
					Predicting what a book might be about	42
T3	Common spelling patterns	44	Understanding capitalisation	50	Retelling stories	52
	Verbs with -ed endings	46	Using capital letters	50	Comparing stories	54
	Verbs with -ing	48			Identifying story elements	54
	Verbs with silent e	48			Anticipating what happens in a story	54
	Verbs with double consonant plus -ing	48			Reading a variety of poems	56, 58
					Composing own poetry	56
					Pairing rhyming words	56
					Comparing and contrasting similar themes in poetry	58
					Collecting favourite poems	58
					Learning poems	58
					Identifying simple questions	60
					Writing simple recounts	60
					Writing own past tense account	60
					Using language of non-fiction texts	62
					Weighing up a topic	62
					Using non-fiction to write a paragraph	62